Magnet Max

Monica Lozano Hughes

Illustrations by Holly Weinstein

KIDS

BROWN BOOKS KIDS

Magnet Max

Brown Books Publishing Group
16250 Knoll Trail Drive, Suite 205
Dallas, Texas 75248
www.BrownBooksKids.com
(972) 381-0009

A New Era in Publishing™

ISBN 978-1-61254-224-9
LCCN 2015932599

Printed in the United States
10 9 8 7 6 5 4 3 2

For more information or to contact the author, please go to
www.MonicaLHughes.com

This book is dedicated to my three children, Adrian, Rachel, and Nick, who have for so many years inspired me to share the joy of reading with them. Without them, I would not have gone into teaching, and, as a result, I would have never developed my love for children's books. I also dedicate this book to my former preschool and kindergarten students, who shared their adventures in learning with me as I read to them year after year. My joy in spreading the love of learning and seeing them fall in love with reading inspired me to write this book.

I would like to thank my husband Gary for believing in me and giving me the support and encouragement to make this dream a reality. To my best friend Denise, who listens to my crazy ideas for songs and books: thanks for your support! I appreciate everyone's willingness to sit with me and listen to my countless questions, such as "Does this look OK?" and "Do the words sound right?"

I also want to thank everyone at the Brown Books Publishing Group for all their help and support, especially Sherry LeVine for looking at my manuscript and considering the possibilities of Magnet Max. Thank you for your encouragement in moving forward with this adventure. I also want to thank Derek Royal and the other editors for helping me to make my manuscript a great story. And special thanks to Holly Weinstein for taking my story, creating such wonderful illustrations, and bringing Magnet Max and Nick to life!

There once was a boy named Magnet Max, who wanted to test what magnets attract.

He loved to explore with objects galore to see what kinds of things would react.

One sunny day, Magnet Max went to play at Nick's house.

Nick did not know this great find.

Max showed him the habit
of his wonderful magnet.

Watching it work blew Nick's mind!

"Wow," Nick yelled. "That's swell!"

The magnet's powers gave him a thrill.

Magnet Max made no reply.
With the wink of an eye,
he made his magnet
attract at his will.

Nick leaped up with glee at the magic,
you see, and asked,
"How do you get them to stick?"

"Magnets give off a magnetic field,"
Max replied.
"They stick to anything, like iron
or steel, real quick!"

"If you please, even nickel and cobalt can be attracted with ease. There are so many possibilities!"

"These are metals that can be part of many things, such as rings, and being magnetic is key."

They looked for metal objects all about, in and out, and found many items that would bind. A paper clip, the refrigerator, a nail, and a bolt, with a jolt, attached to the magnet with force.

Nick exclaimed, "Goodness sakes! I'm amazed at the magic it makes! Can we get it to stick to a horse?"

But a shoe, a ball, a plant, and a doll could not stick to the magnet, of course.

"These items are not magnetic or kinetic," said Max. "They don't have the special force."

The day had gone by as they searched far and wide in the house for more objects to test.

They heard Nick's mom call from way down the hall. "Max, your mom says it's time to go rest."

Max and Nick said, "Aw, man!"

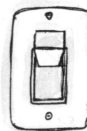

They both looked at the magnet, wanting more to explore.
It was time for Max to go home.

Then Max said, "How about
we hang out tomorrow,
and we can continue our play?"

As Max walked home, he thought of the
things they suggested and tested and
how fun it was to explore today.

Max wanted
to share his tool
that's so cool, so other kids could feel the
same joy. He lay down in bed to relax.

Then closing his eyes,
he dreamed of how wise he
would be as the explorer
Magnet Max!

Author

Monica Lozano Hughes has been an educator for eleven years. This is her first children's book. She is married and has three children. She teaches kindergarten at L.A. Nelson Elementary School in Denton, Texas.

Illustrator

Holly Weinstein received her BFA degree from The College of Art and Design at Lesley University, and she has since illustrated several picture books. She lives in Dallas, Texas, with her husband and two children. Inspired by Magnet Max, Holly and her kids had adventures at home, in their backyard, and inside many local hardware stores collecting as many magnetic materials as they could to include in the illustrations.